CONTENTS

INTRODUCTION

A short history

The sport of inline skating is very young, having only really grown in popularity over the last fifteen years. It has quickly developed into a wide-ranging activity that includes inline speed skating, inline hockey, inline ramp and vertical skating, inline street skating, inline figure skating, inline slalom skating, inline dancing and even inline aerobic classes!

From early ice-skating ...

Inline skating is based on ice-skating – the similarity between the two types of skates is quite obvious. Ice-skating has existed as a sport for a great many years. There are even claims that animal bones were attached to boots as basic 'runners' hundreds of years ago.

A very early ice-skating scene dating from 1570 shows the forerunners for inline skaters.

Radical Sports
INLINE SKATING

Kirk Bizley••••••••••••

www.heinemann.co.uk
Visit our website to find out more information about **Heinemann Library** books.

To order:

 Phone 44 (0) 1865 888066

 Send a fax to 44 (0) 1865 314091

Visit the Heinemann Bookshop at www.heinemann.co.uk to browse our catalogue and order online.

To Joe,

First published in Great Britain by Heinemann Library, Halley Court, Jordan Hill, Oxford OX2 8EJ, a division of Reed Educational and Professional Publishing Ltd.

Heinemann is a registered trademark of Reed Educational & Professional Publishing Limited.

OXFORD   MELBOURNE   AUCKLAND
JOHANNESBURG   BLANTYRE   GABORONE
IBADAN   PORTSMOUTH NH (USA)   CHICAGO

© Reed Educational and Professional Publishing Ltd 2000

The moral right of the proprietor has been asserted.

Designed by Celia Floyd
Originated by HBM Print Ltd, Singapore
Printed in Hong Kong by Wing King Tong

ISBN 0 431 03675 6 (hardback)
04 03 02 01 00
10 9 8 7 6 5 4 3 2 1

ISBN 0 431 03684 5 (paperback)
04 03 02 01 00
10 9 8 7 6 5 4 3 2 1

British Library Cataloguing in Publication Data

Bizley, Kirk
    Inline skating. – (Radical sports)
    1. In-line skating – Juvenile literature
    I. Title
    796.2'1

Acknowledgements

The Publishers would like to thank the following for permission to reproduce photographs:

Mary Evans Picture Library, p. 4; Planet Communications, p. 5 (Lee Mart), p. 10, 29; David Walker, pp. 6, 7, 8, 9, 11, 12, 13, 14, 15, 16, 17, 18, 19, 22, 23, 24, 25, 26; Lee Mart, p. 20, 28.

Cover photograph reproduced with permission of Stockfile/Steven Behr

Our thanks to Stella Capel at G.B. Hockey Inline and Joe Bizley for their comments in the preparation of this book.

Every effort has been made to contact copyright holders of any material reproduced in this book. Any omissions will be rectified in subsequent printings if notice is given to the Publisher.

Any words appearing in the text in bold, **like this**, are explained in the Glossary.

This book aims to cover all the essential techniques of this radical sport but it is important when learning a new sport to get expert tuition and to follow any manufacturers' instructions.

... to the first roller-skate

The roller-skate was invented in 1863 by American, J. L. Plimpton. It had two **axles** with a set of wheels on each. It was an improvement on a wooden version made by a Belgian, Joseph Merlin, in 1760! Roller-skating became very popular in the 20th century, with skate halls and clubs opening up around the world.

Indoor rinks were built from 1930 onwards. In the 1970s, as skates became more efficient through the use of new materials, such as plastic and polyurethane to make the wheels, the popularity of roller-skating increased even more.

Off-season skating

In the 1970s, professional ice-skaters were looking at inline skating as a way of training off season. In 1980 ice-skater Scott Olsen saw some prototype inline skates and formed his own company to make them. The company was called Rollerblade Inc., and today many skaters still refer to their skates as **rollerblades**.

An international sport

The International Inline Skating Association (ILSA) was formed in 1991. By 1994 there were organized competitions taking place in the United States. In 1996, at the Atlanta Olympic Games, it was included as an exhibition sport. Now, there are regular events happening in countries such as Australia, the United States and the UK.

Today inline skating is a growing sport with clubs setting up around the world.

GEARING UP

Before you start you need to think about what you will wear. Safety equipment is very important – it's all too easy to fall over, especially when you are learning.

Liner

The liner should be thick and sturdy with a little extra padding around the toe.

Fastening

Chassis

Wheels

Skates usually come with either three wheels (these are mainly for small women's sizes or children's sizes), or four wheels (men's, medium and large women's sizes and some children's sizes). Your shoe or foot size may decide which type of skate you can buy – make sure you don't buy any which are far too big for you!

Most skates can have extras added after you have bought them and you can always change the type of wheels you have on them.

Heel brake

An important part of your skate. The **brake pad** will need regular checking and replacement.

Helmet

Helmets are not only protective but they can also have reflective tape added to them to make you more visible to other people. Bicycle- or skiing-helmets can be used but make sure when you buy one that it has a safety standard mark on it.

Clothing

Be sensible and remember that you may fall over, so do not leave too much flesh exposed! To avoid over-heating, try to wear clothes that allow air to pass through to your body. To skate well, your body needs to move freely, so avoid wearing anything too tight.

Wrist guards

Some wrist guards have a 'skid pad' that covers the palm of your hand. These are designed so that you can put your hands down if falling or sliding along the ground. Standard guards cover the top of your hand, wrist and part of your forearm. They are designed to reduce the risk of you breaking a wrist.

Elbow pads

These fit around the elbow area. You must make sure that they cover the sides of your elbows and are fitted on firmly so that they don't slip.

Knee pads

These should fit around the sides of the knees and must be fastened securely so that they don't slip.

SAFETY

Protective gear is essential when you are skating – you must wear it!

THE SKATES FOR YOU

Getting advice

When you go to buy your skates you may find the wide choice on offer confusing. So it is important to get good advice. A specialist skate shop is probably the best place to go as you will be able to speak to someone who knows all about the sport.

The choice

These are some of the types of skates that you will find available:

- multi-use skates for recreation, fitness and hockey
- speed skates
- street and stunt skates
- speciality cross-training skates.

Help and advice when trying skates is essential to make sure you get the right pair for you.

If you are a beginner to the sport, the multi-use skates would be the best choice. They are the most adaptable and should suit all your needs.

The cost may well be your major concern. However, remember that you will get what you pay for and a cheap pair of skates may not last for very long. You should be able to buy some with a maker's guarantee – this is worth paying more for because it can save you extra costs in the long run.

Check to see the skates can be modified after you have bought them. You can then change them as you wish depending on what you want to do. For example, you may wish to change the middle wheels if you want to do **grinding**.

Check the fit

The fit of your skates is very important. Try different pairs on to make sure your choice of skates fit properly. Your heels should fit without any feeling that they are sliding up in the boot and there should be enough room for you to be able to move your toes around.

Don't rush your decision and don't worry about trying on several pairs of boots until you find the right ones. Most manufacturers make specialist children's size boots and these may be the best ones for you.

You may choose to buy a second-hand pair of boots from someone who has outgrown them. You can often find these for sale in local papers or magazines. But before you buy them try them out first to make sure they are in a good, usable condition.

Many people advertise their second-hand boots in specialist magazines and this is a good place to find them.

SKATING BASICS

Where can you skate?

This is something you must think about because not all places are suitable for skating. You might even find areas where you are not allowed to skate. Find out about your local area by asking in your local skate shop, looking in skating magazines (or on the Internet) and contacting other local skaters.

Suitable places

The best place to skate is a properly organized inline skate park or arena – you know that you will be welcome there!

You may discover some safe car parking areas that are not used after office hours, usually from early evening onwards or at weekends, and these can be excellent places to learn.

If you are in any doubt about whether or not you should be skating in a particular area, check first! You want to have fun but you must do so safely and legally!

A skate park may have ramps and grinding rails that you can use. Make sure you wear all your protective gear – even if others aren't!

When can you skate?

You should only skate when the conditions are dry. If the ground is wet your skates will slip! Even if you are a good skater you will be taking an unnecessary risk, so don't do it!

As long as it is dry you can skate whenever you like, but if the temperature drops and there is a danger of ice – stop skating.

A SKATER'S RULES

If you do go out skating around the streets, set yourself some rules in order to keep yourself and others from getting injured!

- Always wear your protective gear.
- Always watch where you are going.
- Don't skate too quickly, or race.
- Always approach junctions slowly and with care.
- Give way to pedestrians and other street and road users.
- If it's hot take water to drink and wear sunscreen.

SAFETY FIRST

- You will probably want to get used to your skates on a nice flat, smooth surface. For this reason you may have your eye on a road. Don't be tempted! Roads are very dangerous places to skate!

If you are skating in cold weather wear lots of thin layers rather than one or two thick layers so you don't get too hot.

Don't skate in a built-up area until you have mastered the basic skills of skating! Remember to look both ways when crossing any roads.

Skating is physically demanding and it can be hard work, so you will need to have a good level of general fitness. However, skating is also one of the best ways of getting fit!

Building up stamina

You can start by skating regularly, but be prepared to start off gradually and build up the distance and time you spend skating. Don't go too far – you may discover you are too tired to skate back!

You will not get yourself fit overnight but you will soon be able to go further and for longer as the training pays off. You could also do some jogging or running to help raise your fitness levels. Running uphill is a particularly good method!

Regularly jogging is a good way to build up your stamina for your skating sessions.

SAFETY FIRST

 When stretching don't bounce or make jerky movements as this could injure your muscles.

Warming up

Before each skating session you should **warm-up** to get your body properly prepared for what is to come. It's a good idea to perform some stretching exercises on various parts of your body to prevent injuries. Increased flexibility is important for skaters and this is something you should concentrate on in your warm-up. The more flexible you are the more efficient your skating technique will be.

Stretch out and mobilize all the body areas you will be using when you are skating. The following are examples of good warm-up exercises.

Lower back stretches ············▶

Lying on your back, bend one knee up to your chest and lift your head and shoulders to meet it. Lower yourself. Do this six times before doing the other side.

Neck stretches

Gently pull your head towards your shoulder. Hold for 10 seconds then stretch the other side. ··········

Calf stretches ····················

Stand with one foot in front of the other. Bend your leading leg and lean forward, keeping both feet flat on the floor. Hold this for 10 seconds and relax. Repeat this six times before swapping legs.

COOL OFF

You might find that when you finish a skating session you start to feel rather stiff. To avoid this finish your skate with a cool-down (sometimes called a warm-down). For this, repeat your warm-up but not for so long. This gives your body a chance to recover and return to normal. It also reduces the chance of you feeling stiff and uncomfortable the next day.

THE BASIC STANCE

Ready to begin

The basic skating position you need to learn is called the **ready position**. Stand with your feet 15 to 25 centimetres apart, and your knees bent and pushed forwards. With your hips above your feet, lean slightly forwards from the waist. Put your arms out in front of you and look straight ahead.

In this position you can just **glide** along, without taking steps, and get used to slowly moving forwards. To start off just push off from a wall or rail.

Once you are comfortable with the ready position try taking a few small steps to get moving.

A few small steps

To start yourself moving properly take a few small steps forward, keeping your toes pointed outwards. As soon as you start moving get into the ready position. As you move you might find that your feet are wide apart. Don't worry about this – at first you will need to have them wide apart to keep your balance, but as you get better try to get your feet closer together.

Bend your knees

You must always keep your knees slightly bent as this is the main way of controlling your balance. Leaning slightly forwards will stop you from falling over backwards.

> If you start to wobble, bring your hands into your knees to help you balance yourself again.

Spreading your weight

This should be your **basic stance** when skating. You also need to think about where your weight needs to be distributed in order to stay balanced and stable.

Your weight should be on the balls of your feet. When you are trying to add the small steps to your ready position to get yourself moving, you must remember to shift your weight to the same side as your forward step. As you step, shift your weight so that it's balanced over whichever foot is in contact with the ground.

> While you are skating think about how you move your weight to maintain your balance.

TOP TIP

 Practising the basic stance will help you when you progress to the more advanced moves.

ESSENTIAL TECHNIQUES

A-frame

The **A-frame** position is used for moving slowly. It is similar to skating in the **ready position** but your legs should be spread further apart. Try to spread your legs a little more than shoulder width apart, but not too far or you will fall! Don't let your ankles bend inwards, and keep your skates pointing forwards. You should find that you are skating on the **inside edge** of your skates.

You can practise moving into and out of this position as you move along in your ready position. All you have to do is slowly widen your **stance**.

Pushing and gliding

Gliding is what you were doing when you were first moving at slow speed in your ready position, but now you are going to do it with one foot in front of the other and with the other foot **pushing**.

Point one foot out at an angle of about 45 degrees to get you into a stable position to push against and then glide your other foot forward along the ground. Then bring the back foot up level with the other one and carry on with your glide.

Skating on one leg

You need to be able to do this with both feet. Take it in turns, pushing and gliding with both your left and right foot.

Push with your right foot and glide on your left, then push with your left foot and glide on your right. Now you will feel that you're really skating!

Transferring your weight

Next you must try to balance on each leg as you glide. You should be transferring your weight from the back foot to the front foot as you push and then glide. To learn this, try to do a 'slow motion' version in which you really exaggerate gliding on the one leg only, with your weight balanced on that side.

You must practise this on both sides and with both legs. Soon you will be able to combine all these movements so that as soon as you finish one you start the other, and you will be able to **stride**!

STOPPING

As soon as you can move on your skates you will need to know how to stop! Practise the various ways of stopping at slow speeds so that you are able to stop in any situation.

Wall stop

To do a **wall stop** head towards a wall and stop by absorbing your speed with your hands against the wall. First stand about a metre from the wall, raise your hands and let yourself fall against the wall. Your arms will act like springs to prevent any injury.

You can only use this method at slow speeds – it is very dangerous to move towards any object at high speed and run into it!

Brake pad

Your skates will probably be fitted with **brake pads** at the back. To use these properly you have to put one foot in front of the other and lift the toe of the leading foot, and lean backwards almost in a sitting position. This will help you push your heel down so that the **heel brake** starts to rub along the ground, slowing you down.

It is important to practise braking at very slow speeds, and then gradually build your speed up. Gradually you will learn the distances needed for stopping at different speeds.

V-stop or snowplow

The V-stop or snowplow method of stopping can be used at slow speeds.

Turn your ankles in, or out, to form a V-shape with your skates. Your wheels will act as brake pads and slow you down.

T-stop

The more advanced method of stopping is the **T-stop**. This requires lots of practise because if you don't get it right you could go into a spin! Again, practise at very slow speeds and build up gradually.

When you have one skate forward turn the back skate at a right angle to it. The **friction** of the surface against your skate wheels will slow you down.

TOP TIP

 The T-stop method is not good for your wheels and will wear them down, giving you flattened wheels that will not roll smoothly!

TURNING

You will not want to skate in straight lines all the time. So, to go around corners you must learn to turn on your skates.

Corresponding edges

The **parallel turn** uses the **inside** and **outside edges** of your skates to change direction. Practise by skating on **corresponding edges**. This means that you skate on the inside edge of one skate while you are on the outside edge of the other. At the same time, you must lean towards the outside edge side. As a result, you will move in that direction.

Practise for the parallel turn by skating on corresponding edges.

Parallel turn

Once you have mastered this technique you will be able to do a full **parallel turn**. Make sure that you are on corresponding edges and tilt your body, swinging your arms and shoulders to the same side. To turn right you make sure your right skate is forward on the outside edge and you tilt to the right. To turn left you do the same with your left skate and tilt left.

Don't try to turn too sharply at first – build yourself up with small turns.

Scooter

Using the **scooter** method you will be able to move around in small circles. Push with your back foot sideways on and **glide** with your front foot. Make sure your front foot stays on the ground but on the outside edge.

By swapping feet you will be able to go round in clockwise and anticlockwise circles.

Crossovers

You are now ready to go on to the best, and most exciting method of turning – **crossovers**! You can do very tight turns with this method and turn with greater speed. To turn right, cross the left skate over the right and push with the right skate before picking it up again and bringing it back together with the left. To turn left, work with the opposite feet.

Being able to turn using the crossover method makes you feel that you're really skating.

TAKING IT FURTHER

Inline skating has developed very quickly as a sport and there are now many types of inline skating to choose from.

Fun on the ramps

Lots of skaters enjoy using specially constructed ramps. Originally many of these ramps were made for skateboarders and BMX riders, but they are just as much fun for inline skaters.

Your local skating club may have ramps that you can use.

You can learn to slide along kerbs and poles, which are usually at skate arenas, too!

Grinding

A popular technique amongst skaters is **grinding**. To do this you need to adjust your skates by putting two small wheels in the middle of your skates and adding **grinding plates** to the edges of your skates. When using ramps or grinding make sure you wear all your protective gear.

Aggressive skating

Skating on ramps and grinding are called **aggressive skating**. There are organized competitions in some areas for skaters to display these and other types of tricks.

Professional coaching

If you do decide to take up inline skating seriously you should try to get some correct and professional coaching. Make enquiries about organized local clubs and any coaching schemes they may run. Specialist magazines and your local skate shop will be good sources of information, too.

Competing for fun

Playing inline hockey is a good way of improving your skating skills while learning a competitive organized sport as well! The inline hockey scene is expanding quickly so you may well find a team in your area.

The International **Ice Hockey** Federation have established rules for inline hockey which put emphasis on skill and technique.

INLINE HOCKEY

Inline hockey is one of the most popular and fastest growing sports associated with inline skating.

Its roots

The sport began as **street hockey**, which is not a formally organized game – it's played anywhere the players think suitable. Inline hockey has close links with the sport of **ice hockey**, too.

The game

There are a maximum of 16 players in a team and 4 players plus the goalkeeper are on the playing surface at any one time. Either a **puck** or ball is used and teams attempt to shoot this into netted goals.

Equipment

If you are considering taking up inline hockey then there are some extra pieces of equipment you will have to buy.

Goalkeepers

Goalkeepers have to wear a great deal of protective equipment. As this is very expensive it is best to join an organized club which might have all the equipment you need to wear.

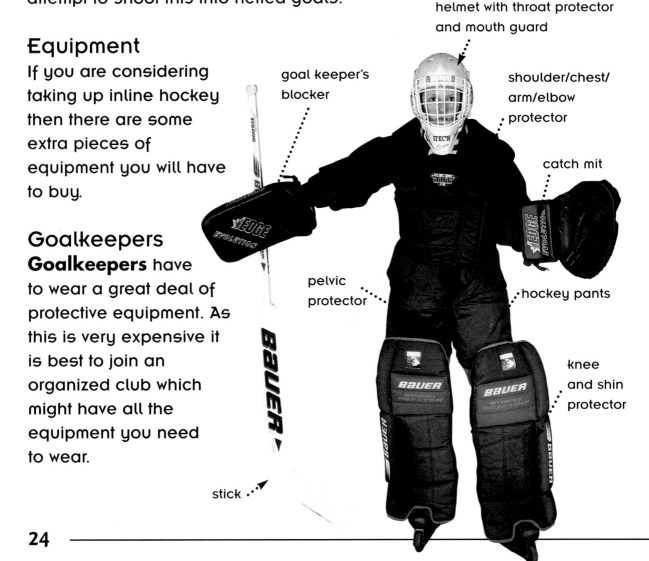

helmet with throat protector and mouth guard

goal keeper's blocker

shoulder/chest/arm/elbow protector

catch mit

pelvic protector

hockey pants

knee and shin protector

stick

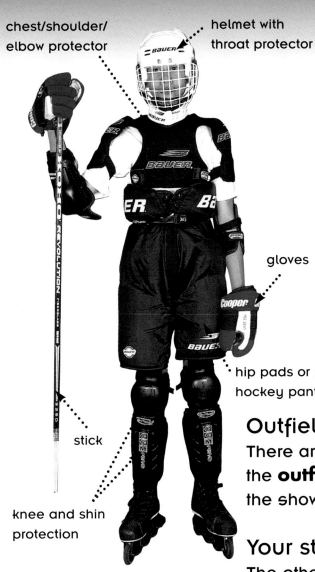

chest/shoulder/
elbow protector

helmet with
throat protector

gloves

hip pads or padded
hockey pants

stick

knee and shin
protection

Outfield players

There are also equipment requirements for the **outfield players**. You should wear all the shown protective equipment.

Your stick

The other piece of vital equipment is, of course, your stick! You will have quite a large range to choose from. They are made of aluminium, graphite, wood, and other composite materials. You will probably also have a choice of styles. The wooden ones are cheaper but the graphite ones are stronger and likely to last longer.

Ther are many types of stick to choose from.

CARING FOR YOUR EQUIPMENT

You will need to carry out a little bit of maintenance quite often on your skates, so be prepared.

Essential tools

When you buy your skates you should get a set of basic tools with them. If not, you should buy some from a skate shop. These tools are very important as they are made specifically for the job – don't try to use other household tools instead!

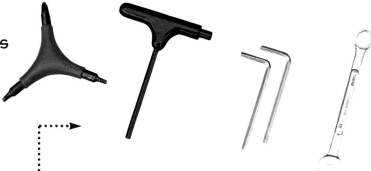

These specially adapted screwdrivers, Allen keys and spanners can adjust all the equipment on your skates.

Brake pads

Your **heel brake** needs checking regularly and must be replaced when it wears down. Many of the **brake pads** have a **wear line** that shows when the pad has worn down too far, at which point you must replace the pad. Heel brakes and pads are quickly and easily changed. You can easily do this yourself using a screwdriver or the tool provided by the manufacturer.

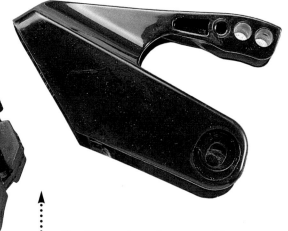

Brake pad replacement is an important part of your skate maintenance.

SAFETY FIRST

Worn brakes mean less efficient stopping – they must be checked and changed regularly.

Wheels

You also need to check your wheels for wear and you should regularly rotate them into different positions on your skates. The wheels will wear down on one side, or edge, and if they wear down too far the only thing you can do is replace them. Rotated wheels will last up to four times longer than ones just left in place! It's a quick and easy job to remove all the wheels and put them back in different positions, or even on a different skate. At the same time clean off any dirt from the fittings around them.

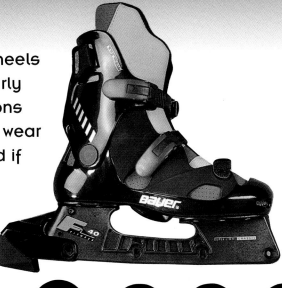

Regularly check, rotate and replace the wheels on your skates.

Bearings

In the middle section of your wheels, inside the **hub**, are the **bearings**. These need maintaining and sometimes replacing. Bearings are small, round metal balls contained in a metal case. They allow your wheels to spin freely and smoothly.

When you remove your wheels for rotation you should clean off any excess grease around the hub and around the bearings. If you notice that your wheels are getting stiff, not spinning smoothly or making strange noises it's probably time to replace the bearings. You can buy new ones (and a **bearing tool** for getting the old bearings out). It is easy to pop the old ones out and put the new ones in.

A bearing tool and the bearings which fit into the central hub of your wheels.

SKATING EVENTS

Inline skating is still in the early stages of becoming formally organized with governing bodies and organized competitions. If you want to find out about any competitions in your area check specialist skating magazines and local skate shops for details – you may be surprised to discover how much is happening!

Championships

There are organized championships for both British and European titles for distance and speed skating.

In the British Championships there are events for all age groups from 6 to 10 year old boys and girls, right through to senior men's and women's races. The race distances ranged from 300 metre sprints to 20,000 metres!

In 1998 the European Cadet and Junior Championships were held in Lisbon, Portugal, with various individual and relay events. Thirteen different European nations took part.

A competitor at an **aggressive skaters** association competition.

International events

Internationally, inline skating is becoming more organized and in the United States there are two competition series which are becoming popular. These are the National Inline Skate Series (NISS) and the International Inline Skate Series (IISS). The NISS started in 1993 with display shows and developed into a properly organized series of events around the southwest coast of the United States.

The success of this led to the international tour which now features ten different international venues around the world. The champion from each one gets a chance to compete in the Grand Final followed by the NISS finals which take place during September at Venice Beach, USA.

Aggressive skaters association

The Aggressive Skaters Association (ASA) has organized a professional tour in which both amateur and professional competitions are held throughout the world.

Hockey

Also in the United States, a Pro Beach Hockey series has been launched which is a version of inline hockey. This has been backed by one of the specialist cable TV sports channels so is guaranteed to be well publicized.

A Pro Beach Hockey game underway in the United States.

GLOSSARY

A-frame   a skating position with legs wide apart

aggressive skating   skating using ramps, jumps and tricks

axle   the supporting shaft on which the wheels turn

basic stance   a balanced skating position

bearings   the sealed units containing ball-bearings which allow the skate's wheels to rotate smoothly

bearing tool   a specially designed tool to remove bearings

brake pad   the rubber pad that makes up the heel brake

corresponding edges   with one set of skate wheels tilted inwards while the others are tilted outwards

crossovers   a method of turning in which the skates cross over each other

friction   a force generated when two surfaces rub against each other. Skaters use the friction between a brake pad or wheel and the floor surface to slow down

glide   moving smoothly forwards or backwards on the skates

goalkeeper   designated player who must play in the goal area

grinding   sliding along a surface such as a kerb or a pole

grinding plates   protective plates fitted to the sides of skates to allow grinding

heel brake   a brake stopper fitted at the rear of each skate

hub   inner section of each wheel

ice hockey   a form of hockey played on an indoor hockey rink with set rules and regulations

inside edge   the edge of the wheel facing the inside of the skater

outfield player   any player on the playing surface, other than the goalkeeper

outside edge   the edge of the wheel facing away from the skater

parallel turn   a method of turning or cornering using the inside and outside skate edges

puck   a rubber disk used like a ball in hockey

pushing   shifting the skates forward with a pushing movement

ready position   a basic, balanced skating position

rollerblades   another common term for inline skates

scooter   skating technique for skating in small circles

snowplow   a skating technique for slowing and stopping

stance   your body position when skating

street hockey   an 'unofficial' game of hockey played outside with an arranged set of rules

stride   long, smooth skating movements

T-stop   a method of braking and stopping by turning one skate at right angles to the other

V-stop   a method of braking and stopping by angling the skates either in or out in a V-shape

wall stop   a method of stopping against a wall, using your arms as cushioning

warm-up   preparing the body for the physical activity to come

wear line   a line on brake pads that show when they have worn dangerously low

USEFUL ADDRESSES

GB Hockey Inline
The Arena
Deeside Leisure Centre
Chester Road West
Queensferry
Flintshire
CH5 1SA
Tel/fax: 01244 813938
e-mail: Skateste@aol.com
Website: www.eiha.co.uk

London Rollercity
Stonehill Business Park
Lea Valley Trading Estate
North Circular Road
Edmonton
London N18
0181 807 5511

Manchester Bones Skatepark
Canal Street
Stockport
Cheshire

Roller Sports Australia
PO Box 9
Roma Street
Brisbane
Queensland
Australia 4003

FURTHER READING

Books

Inline Skating Basics, Sam Miller, Sterling

Inline Skating, Bruce Curtis, Sterling

Inline Skating, Jeremy Evans, Parragon

The Young Inline skater, Chris Edwards, Dorling Kindersley

Magazine

Inline Skatermag, Arcwind Ltd

Websites

www.eiha.co.uk – GB Hockey Inline

www.skate.ch

www.aggressive.com

INDEX